Contents

Healthy Neighbourhoods

Natasha Gowman

King's Fund

Published by
King's Fund Publishing
11–13 Cavendish Square
London W1M 0AN

First published 1999

ISBN 1 85717 250 7
A CIP catalogue record for this book is available from the British Library

Available from:

King's Fund Bookshop
11–13 Cavendish Square
London W1M 0AN

Tel: 0171 307 2591
Fax: 0171 307 2591

This report has been produced to disseminate research findings and promote good practice in health and social care. It has not been professionally copy-edited or proof-read.

Printed and bound in Great Britain

The King's Fund Public Health Programme

The Public Health Programme aims to find ways of reducing inequalities in health and improving the general health of the population, especially in London. The Programme is focused on the ways in which health is affected not only by health services, but also by the activities of a wide range of public, voluntary and commercial organisations, and individuals and groups at national and local levels. Above all, it is concerned with the links between all these factors and how they interact to influence the health of people and populations.

The programme team carry out research, analysis and developmental work with a view to influencing both policy and practice. We aim to stimulate ideas, innovation, and informed debate among policy makers, opinion formers, practitioners in public health, local government, voluntary and private sectors, as well as with the wider public. We disseminate our work through seminars and conferences and through the general and specialist media, as well as via the King's Fund website and publishing in print.

The Public Health Team:
Anna Coote, Programme Director
Liz Kendall, Fellow
Natasha Gowman, Research Officer
Pat Tawn, Administrator

Acknowledgements

Healthy neighbourhoods were the subject of discussion at a King's Fund Public Health seminar held on December 14th 1998. Thanks are due to everyone who participated in the seminar, and to the individuals who facilitated visits to their local projects, for sharing their knowledge, experiences, insights and information.

Executive summary

The public health Green Paper, *Our Healthier Nation*, proposed using the concept of healthy settings to provide a focus for action aimed at improving health and reducing health inequalities. Three settings were suggested: Healthy Schools, focusing on children; Healthy Workplaces, focusing on adults; and Healthy Neighbourhoods, focusing on older people. *Healthy Neighbourhoods* examines the potential of the neighbourhood setting, and puts forward realistic suggestions which could help Government, local agencies and residents to work together to develop healthier neighbourhoods.

What are healthy neighbourhoods?

A healthy neighbourhood is about the issues that matter to local people – and which are now accepted as affecting health. *Healthy Neighbourhoods* brings together a range of models which provide different definitions of neighbourhoods, and approaches to working with and within them, such as the World Health Organisation's Healthy Cities Project and healthy neighbourhoods in Australia. Local people's own perceptions of what makes a healthy neighbourhood are also considered, and the report describes how these views have informed the development of neighbourhood projects. This information is combined to provide some suggestions about the defining characteristics of a healthy neighbourhood:

- ◆ **A healthy neighbourhood is:**
  - safe
  - clean
  - inclusive
  - confident
  - creative
  - connected

There are people for whom the neighbourhood setting has particular significance. For people whose mobility is restricted for a range of reasons – low incomes, physical frailty, problems with transport, or caring responsibilities for example - the immediate surroundings of the home and neighbourhood can form the greater part of a fairly small world. *Healthy Neighbourhoods* identifies the groups of people of people to whom the neighbourhood means most, and argues that policies and action pursued at neighbourhood level could make an important contribution to improving health – and reducing inequalities in health – for:

- young families
- older people
- people on low incomes
- people who are less mobile

Importantly, the report demonstrates that these people are found in all kinds of neighbourhoods, rather than being concentrated in the "worst estates" currently receiving so much attention. The best way to improve health for these groups is to work with whole neighbourhoods of every kind, and then target within them. Healthy neighbourhoods should be everyone's initiative.

Joining up neighbourhood policy

The report considers the approaches, and implications, of a number of new and recent initiatives from other policy spheres which have a neighbourhood focus, including:

- Sure Start
- The New Deal for Communities
- Local Agenda 21
- Healthy Living Centres
- Supporting Families

Healthy neighbourhoods argues that the contribution that these and similar initiatives can make to health, well being and quality of life is too often overlooked. The report asserts that the Government's new strategy for public health should play a vital role in joining up such policies to maximise the public health.

Developing healthy neighbourhoods

But the role of the neighbourhood setting could be extended beyond providing a focus for policy co-ordination. A number of areas around the country are already demonstrating the progress that can be made when local people and agencies from all sectors come together to address residents' concerns, and improve the health of individuals and their communities. *Healthy Neighbourhoods* describes projects already being undertaken in five different places around the country, including:

◆ **Beckton Community Health Project**

Residents from all sections of this London docklands community are working with local government, health services, voluntary organisations and the private sector to improve their social and physical environment, with the aim of reducing stress and isolation. As a first step they have renovated a pond, providing a restful space for local people to enjoy.

◆ **Matson Neighbourhood Project, Gloucestershire**

One of a network of healthy villages, residents of the Matson neighbourhood have established a range of facilities and services in response to local needs. These include a home shopping service and a lunch club (with taxi service) for older people, an IT skills training centre, an after school club and a drop in centre for people with mental health problems.

A contract for healthy neighbourhoods

Healthy Neighbourhoods proposes a number of ways that the healthy neighbourhood concept could be developed to support practical neighbourhood action to improve health, using the contract for health set out in *Our Healthier Nation*:

◆ **Government could:**
- provide guidance
- identify and encourage neighbourhoods where action is most needed
- establish a support network and information exchange
- acknowledge and reward effort and success

- ♦ **Neighbourhoods could:**
    - secure community involvement
    - form local partnerships
    - establish a focal point for action
    - develop a flagship project
    - set clear objectives

- ♦ **People could:**
    - take responsibility for maintaining the positive aspects of their neighbourhood
    - get involved in local action
    - contribute their skills, knowledge and time

The further development of the neighbourhood setting offers an opportunity for Government and local agencies to work with local people to address the health issues that matter to them. By reaching out to people in the places they live, healthy neighbourhoods could achieve significant health gains among people too often excluded by traditional public health approaches.

Introduction

The Green Paper *Our Healthier Nation* identifies healthy neighbourhoods as one of three settings, together with schools and workplaces, in which the Government's new contract for health will be fulfilled. Interventions made in the neighbourhood setting have the potential to make a real impact on health, by reaching people and places in ways quite different to traditional health interventions. Health is fundamentally linked with where people live: their homes, communities and surroundings. Poor health and poor neighbourhoods go hand in hand, but in addition to problems even the poorest neighbourhoods also have considerable potential. The success of initiatives aimed at promoting healthy neighbourhoods will rely on their ability to work with the resources that already exist within communities - local knowledge, experience and skills, plus existing services and amenities. In doing so they will need to be innovative, and prepared to try new ways of working. This will require a policy framework which provides clarity of purpose without prescription, and which supports and enables development. The neighbourhood setting could play an important role in bringing together the range of initiatives proposed in *Our Healthier Nation,* unifying the Government's public health strategy.

Purpose and structure

The timing of this report, between the publication of the Green and White papers, provides a window of opportunity in which to explore the healthy neighbourhood concept and what it could come to represent. The report, and the research which underpinned it, aims to contribute ideas about how healthy neighbourhoods could be defined and identified, and to consider what the essential components of a healthy neighbourhood are. Moving beyond definitions, this report considers the steps that need to be taken if the healthy neighbourhood concept is to become a practical reality.

The paper begins with an overview of the healthy settings proposed in *Our Healthier Nation*, and briefly discusses the healthy settings concept. Section one also considers what neighbourhoods mean to different groups of people, and the consequences this may have for policy development. Section two draws on some existing initiatives with a geographical focus, such as the WHO Healthy Cities Project, to see what lessons can be learned from these experiences. A number of ongoing and new policy initiatives also have relevance to the healthy neighbourhood setting, and these are outlined in section three. Key initiatives (including the New Deal for Communities, Local Agenda 21, and the recently announced sustainability indicators) are analysed, and the definitions and approaches they apply are highlighted. Some practical examples of measures that are helping to improve the health of neighbourhoods are outlined in section four, with descriptions of five projects working with contrasting neighbourhoods and different approaches. Finally, section five brings together the competing views about what makes a neighbourhood and suggests some defining characteristics of a healthy neighbourhood. The section concludes with a series of recommendations about how the healthy neighbourhood strategy could most usefully be developed, and uses the Government's new contract for health as a model to identify the contributions that could be made by Government, neighbourhoods and local people.

Section One: Healthy settings

Our Healthier Nation

The public health Green Paper *Our Healthier Nation* proposes the use of healthy settings as a focus for targeted interventions to achieve heath gain[1]. The three settings identified (schools, workplaces and neighbourhoods) are seen as providing a focus for inter-departmental Government action and local partnership. *Our Healthier Nation* sets out a range of possible directions along which the healthy neighbourhood setting could develop. Proposals are put forward aimed at meeting the needs of older people, improving the health of whole communities, and tackling health inequalities. The Green Paper does not provide a definition of a neighbourhood, but states that Health Improvement Programmes will need to "identify those parts of their areas which need particular effort in order to improve the health of the local population".

Healthy schools are intended to provide a setting for improving the health of children, not just through health education but by equipping them with the life skills and knowledge to take care of their health throughout their lives. In July 1998 a network of eight Healthy Schools pilot sites was established, each receiving £150,000 to develop initiatives and provide models of what works. Healthy Schools will require joint working between health and local authorities, and a Healthy Schools award, "Investors in Health", has been established.

The Healthy Workplace setting has two aims: firstly, to improve the overall health of the workforce and secondly to ensure that people are protected from workplace hazards.

For the purposes of the *Our Healthier Nation* strategy a Healthy Workplace has been defined as follows:

◆ **A workplace is anywhere where people work ... a healthy workplace is therefore:**

- a place where health risks are recognised and controlled if they cannot be removed
- a place where work design is compatible with people's health needs and limitations
- an environment that supports the promotion of healthy lifestyles
- a place where employees and employers recognise their responsibility for their health and the health of their colleagues

Source: *Target*, Issue 30, September 1998

National leadership on healthy schools policy is to be provided by the Departments of Health and Education, and workplace policy is to be developed by the Department of Health in conjunction with the Health and Safety Executive. It is not yet clear which departments or non-governmental bodies may be involved in leading the healthy neighbourhoods strategy.

The inclusion of the neighbourhood setting in the Green Paper is clearly intended to bridge the gap between the populations served by healthy workplaces and healthy schools. The Green Paper variously mentions a number of groups which the healthy neighbourhoods initiative should aim to focus on, including older people, the jobless, people working in the home as carers. Can the neighbourhood setting be developed sufficiently to fulfil this role? A public health policy that is, in practice, focused mainly on people in schools and workplaces runs the risk of compounding existing inequalities by leaving unmet the needs of people excluded for whatever reasons from these settings – a point reinforced by the Acheson Report. Every school and workplace is located within a neighbourhood – although not all neighbourhoods will contain one or both. In this sense, neighbourhoods form an overarching setting which has the potential to unify the *Our Healthier Nation* strategy, making it truly nation-wide.

The healthy settings concept

The identification of settings as a focus for improving health has long been advocated by the World Health Organisation[2]. Most recently, target thirteen of the newly devised 21 targets for the 21st century states:

> *By the year 2015, people in the region should have greater opportunities to live in healthy physical and social environments at home, at school, at the workplace and in the local community.*

WHO has identified the following settings as having a role in supporting health[3]. Conditions in each of them are seen as having equal or greater impact on the health of local people than the availability of health care. The settings identified are:

◆ **WHO Healthy settings**
- home, village or neighbourhood
- school
- workplace
- food markets
- city and district
- sport and leisure

Of the settings identified above, the first three are addressed by the settings outlined in *Our Healthier Nation*. The majority of the remaining settings may potentially be addressed by other recently announced initiatives. The Social Exclusion Unit's Action Team on Access to Shops will be looking at the food market, with the impetus for action in this area reinforced by the recommendations of the Acheson report. And a range of initiatives, including the New Deal for Communities and the Urban Task Force will have the opportunity to address the city and district setting. Sports and leisure therefore remain unattached to any particular healthy setting at present. In fact, a strong argument can be made for access to sports and leisure facilities forming a central building block of a healthy neighbourhood. Affordable, accessible and culturally appropriate recreation and exercise facilities can have an impact on the physical and psychological health of residents of all ages, and the provision of these amenities could be located quite logically within the healthy neighbourhood policy framework.

WHO makes clear links between the healthy settings concept and a number of the challenges facing the "new public health", and argues that the healthy settings concept demonstrates particular strengths in addressing the challenge of community participation and intersectoral co-operation for health. They state that the involvement and commitment of local people is more readily secured using the healthy settings concept because there is already an attachment to and interest in the area.

Unhealthy neighbourhoods: inequalities in health

It is possible to construct a picture of an "unhealthy neighbourhood" based on available statistics. The recent report of the Independent Inquiry into Inequalities in Health (the "Acheson Report") shows that poor neighbourhoods are characterised by poor health. [4] The report vividly illustrates the ways in which every aspect of health – mortality, years of life lost and morbidity – is measurably worse for people living in deprived circumstances. And the report points out that deprived areas also tend to have a number of other features in common, including higher rates of crime and accidents in and around the home, low levels of educational achievement and high levels of school exclusion and truancy. The healthy neighbourhood setting has the potential to reach these very deprived areas, and bring about an improvement in the health of the people living there.

The report recommends action on three crucial fronts to reduce inequalities in health, all of which underline the potential of the neighbourhood setting:

◆ **The Acheson Report**

- all policies likely to have an impact on health should be evaluated in terms of their impact on health inequalities
- a high priority should be given to the health of families with children
- further steps should be taken to reduce income inequalities and improve the living standards of poor households

The Acheson report considers how inequalities in health can be tackled in all three of the healthy settings identified in *Our Healthier Nation*. In relation to the neighbourhood, the report considers the role of housing and the environment in shaping health, but also highlights the importance of social networks. The report also places schools firmly in the context of the broader community, calling for stronger school/community links, and points out the contribution that initiatives such as health promoting schools can make to the long term well being of whole communities, by tackling issues such as poor nutrition, stress and truancy.

A list highlighting the recommendations of the Independent Inquiry which have particular relevance to the healthy neighbourhood setting is attached as Appendix 1.

People and places

Healthy neighbourhoods should be concerned with reducing inequalities in health. But the differences that exist between and within neighbourhoods present policy makers with a particular challenge in this respect. Whilst neighbourhoods can form geographical clusters of particular socio-economic or cultural groups, one type of neighbourhood may not contain all of the groups of people that policy makers wish to reach – such as older people or young families with low incomes. The different patterns of geographical distribution for these two groups' geographical dispersal are especially striking.

The English House Condition Survey 1996 revealed that older people live in many different kinds of housing, including owner occupation and accommodation rented privately or from housing associations. The survey also looked at the position of older people living in "poor neighbourhoods", defined as "concentrations of housing in substantial disrepair; vacant and derelict housing; and other forms of neglect or misuse such as vandalism, graffiti and rubbish" – in other words, the kinds of "worst estates" being targeted by the New Deal for Communities. Less than 5% of older people were found to be living in these conditions, but the circumstances of their peers in more affluent neighbourhoods scarcely provide cause for complacency. Single older people are the most likely group to live in properties which are in a poor condition, and these properties may be located in relatively affluent neighbourhoods[5].

Young families with low incomes by contrast tend to be clustered much more tightly, and are more likely to live in local authority housing. The "worst estates" which are to be the focus of Government initiatives such as the New Deal for Communities and Sure Start have been shown to have relatively high child densities (the proportion of the population aged 16 or under) compared to the rest of the population, and generally more youthful residents overall[6].

Both older people and young families on low incomes could form a legitimate focus for the healthy neighbourhoods initiative, not least because they are unlikely to have significant contact with the school or workplace settings. But a policy focus on just one kind of neighbourhood will not reach both old and young.

The differences within neighbourhoods are also instructive. The way people view their neighbourhoods is determined by a range of factors – income, the availability of transport, caring responsibilities, employment, age, and physical condition – that effectively set that individual's "horizons". The extent to which someone is able to mobilise within and beyond the boundaries of their neighbourhood is central to the importance that the neighbourhood has for them. So the relationship between individuals and their neighbourhoods varies over time, according to life stages and circumstances. For some people, such as adults spending much of the day away from the home at work or travelling, the home and its surroundings may represent a comparatively small part of their world. Other people, for the reasons already mentioned, can have a very localised view of their neighbourhood, perceiving few links with the wider world. In their work with older people the Camden Healthy Cities Project found that even where services to promote mobility among frail elderly people were in existence, this did not always enhance neighbourhood ties. Dial-a-Ride schemes, for instance, are seen by some older people as whisking them away from their home to a day centre or event on the other side of town, without bringing them into contact with any of their neighbours[7].

Children too can have a distinctive view of their neighbourhood. The Children's Society's Patio Project in Rotherham has found that children use, and perceive, their surroundings in quite a different way to the adults also living there. The Patio Project uncovered a great deal of ingenuity and creativity being applied to finding places to play, and concluded: "Neighbourhood will mean different things for different children, but common to all of them will be a need for territory and belonging".[8]

Summary

The different concepts and definitions of the neighbourhood setting outlined above consistently view the neighbourhood as the setting which encompasses the important aspects of community life, including the activities that take place in schools and workplaces. Healthy neighbourhoods should not be seen as one of a number of settings, but as the cohesive force which binds other settings together.

Choices about the types of neighbourhoods included in an initiative to promote healthier neighbourhoods will be instrumental in determining which sections of the population are to be reached - and which excluded. Too narrow a focus on one type of neighbourhood, or one population group, will result in a patchy and incomplete strategy which fails to reach precisely those people it was intended for.

References

[1] Department of Health, *Our Healthier Nation: a contract for health,* London, The Stationery Office, 1998.
[2] World Health Organisation Regional Office for Europe *Health 21 – The Health for All Policy for the European Region – 21 Targets for the 21st Century*, Copenhagen, 1998
[3] Sources: Greg Goldstein and Ilona Kickbusch, "A healthy city is a better city", *World Health*, 49:1, Jan-Feb 1996 and The World Health Organisation, *Sustainable Development and Healthy Environments, Programme for*

the Promotion of Environmental Health: Settings for Health, http://www.who.int/peh/hlthcit/setting.htm (20.11.98)

[4] D. Acheson, *Report of the Independent Inquiry into Inequalities in Health*, The Stationery Office,1998.

[5] Best, R. "The Housing Dimension", in Benzeval, Judge and Whitehead, eds., *Tackling Inequalities in Health*, London, The King's Fund, 1995.

[6] Report by the Social Exclusion Unit, *Bringing Britain Together: a national strategy for neighbourhood renewal*, 1998.

[7] Camden Healthy Cities Project, *Quality of Life Conference for Older People and their Carers*, Report of a conference held on 21.9.96, London, 1996

[8] Community Development Foundation, *Involving Children in Neighbourhood Regeneration*, a briefing paper for Chief Executive Departments of Local Authorities, 1998.

Section Two: Models

Although the healthy settings concept is relatively new, there are some existing initiatives from which lessons can be learned. Two models are considered (The WHO Healthy Cities Project, and the Australian Healthy Neighbourhoods initiative), and the criteria these initiatives have used to identify the characteristics of their particular healthy setting are highlighted.

The WHO Healthy Cities Project

The WHO Healthy Cities Project was established in 1987, and will soon be entering its third phase. The project is the main vehicle for translating WHO's Health For All strategy into action[9]. Within the UK four areas, Liverpool, Camden, Belfast and Glasgow, have established Healthy Cities projects. In all, over 30 cities in Europe and many more world-wide are currently involved. By WHO's own definition:

> *A Healthy City is one that is continually creating and improving those physical and social environments and expanding those community resources which enable people to mutually support each other in performing all the functions of life and in developing to their maximum potential*[10]

Agis Tsouros highlights the fact that healthy cities need to be defined in terms of both process and outcome. The definition, therefore, should not be concerned so much with the level of health that has been achieved, as with the action that is being undertaken to improve, maintain and promote health.

♦ **Characteristics of a Healthy City :**

- a clean, safe physical environment of high quality (including housing quality)
- an ecosystem that is stable now and sustainable in the long term
- a strong, mutually supportive, integrated and non-exploitative community
- a high degree of participation and control by the public in over the decisions affecting their lives, health and wellbeing
- the meeting of basic needs (for food, water, shelter, income, safety and work) for all the city's people
- access to a wide variety of experiences and resources, with the chance for a wide variety of contact, interaction and communication
- a diverse, vital and innovative city economy
- the encouragement of connectedness with the past, with the cultural and biological heritage of city dwellers and with other groups and individuals
- a form that is compatible with and enhances the preceding characteristics
- an optimum level of appropriate public health and sick care services accessible to all
- high health status (high levels of positive health and low levels of disease)

Source: *Twenty steps for developing a Healthy Cities project* [11]

As a well established and highly influential initiative, a number of conclusions can be drawn from evaluations and reflections on more than ten years of Healthy Cities experience. Reflecting on progress in 1996, Agis Tsouros came to two instructive conclusions. Firstly, it is not possible to draw up a single recipe for every city: the diversity of Healthy Cities is their strength. Secondly, project ownership is crucial: politicians of all parties and different central and local departments must be willing to share power[12].

The UK Health For All Network was established in 1987 as part of the WHO's *Health For All 2000* initiative. It supports the Healthy Cities Network, and also acts as a central point of contact, information and support for members in all areas who are working towards the principles of *Health For All* through other local initiatives.

Australian Healthy Neighbourhoods

The European Healthy Cities model has also been applied in some areas of Australia. Because Australia has fewer cities, but still has an essentially European culture and societal structure, the Healthy Cities model was adapted to suit Australian centres of population. In their review of the Australian experience of community and neighbourhood focused initiatives, Harris and Wills identify six dimensions of healthy local communities. They emphasise that the dimensions should be seen as interacting, although each one may be individually addressed by separate interventions. The dimensions are as follows:

◆ **Characteristics of an Australian healthy neighbourhood:**
- a healthy population – the people in the community have low levels of preventable mortality and morbidity
- a population with the knowledge, skills and resources to make choices that will promote health
- organisational settings within the community that promote the health of the population they serve
- a high-quality natural environment – people have access to a safe water supply, clean air, open space and low levels of contamination
- a health promoting man-made environment – the houses and neighbourhoods in which people live are safe, are appropriate to their needs, and allow access to community services
- social, economic and political environments that promote health – people live in communities that value them and their beliefs, and have access to employment opportunities and to processes that allow them to participate in the decisions that will affect their lives

Source: *Harris and Wills, Developing healthy local communities at local government level*

Two points stand out from the list above. The first is that the healthy community is seen as encompassing healthy schools and workplaces: the three are seen as interdependent. The second point concerns the value placed on active participation by people within the community, which is not evident to the same extent as in the WHO model.

An evaluation of the first wave of Australian projects conducted in 1992 concluded that there was a tendency for the content of the healthy cities programme to be viewed with suspicion by local government because of a lack of clarity about the goals and content of the programme[13]. This is a finding which could have relevance to the UK healthy neighbourhoods strategy: in the absence of a clear definition, agencies may be wary of signing up to a portmanteau initiative. Where the potential of the programme was viewed more favourably, difficulties were encountered in arriving at shared objectives which were meaningful to all involved. The evaluation also highlighted the problems of attempting to secure public participation and intersectoral action simultaneously in the local political environment.

Summary

The experiences of these existing models highlight some important issues which will need to be addressed if a strategy to promote healthy neighbourhoods is to attain its potential. Will those involved allow neighbourhoods the flexibility they need to engage with local circumstances and priorities? Can a strategy to promote healthy neighbourhoods accommodate the active involvement of community organisations, individual residents, local politicians and agencies – with all the tensions that could involve? And what will persuade and encourage all of these players to overcome their scepticism and join forces to create healthier neighbourhoods?

[13] A.Whelan, R.Mohr, S.Short, "Waving or drowning? Evaluation of the National Secretariat, Healthy Cities Australia", Sydney: Australian Community Health Association, 1992 cited in Elizabeth Harris and Jenny Wills, "Developing healthy local communities at local government level: lessons from the past decade", *Australian and New Zealand Journal of Public Health*, 1997, 21:4

Section Three: Local visions

In addition to the broad national and international strategies described above, there are a growing number of domestic policy initiatives that have a local, area based focus. Developments in the fields of sustainability and regeneration are set out below. These policies are assessed to see what pointers these might provide for shaping a healthy neighbourhoods strategy, and also for what they tell us about the environment in which moves to develop healthy neighbourhoods will be taking place. The various policy initiatives are also considered in relation to the connections they have with health, and the opportunities they afford for "joining up" policy in this context.

Sustainability

The underpinning principle of sustainability is that the needs of current populations should not be met through ways that compromise the ability of future generations to meet their own needs from the earth's resources[14]. In terms of health, a simplistic definition would hold that "*My* health should not be achieved at the expense of *your* health".

Local Agenda 21

Local Agenda 21 represents the best example of action aimed at promoting sustainability in the UK. The principles of Local Agenda 21 were framed in the course of the United Nations Conference on Environment and Development (the "earth summit") held in Rio in 1992. The Rio conference signalled a widening of the debate around sustainability, and marked a new commitment to ensuring that social and economic factors were considered in relation to sustainability, augmenting the previously narrow emphasis on environmental factors.

Local Agenda 21 represents the way in which the commitments given at the Rio conference can be taken forward at local level, with local government taking the lead in turning the strategy into action. The UK Government has recently made it a requirement for all local authorities to put in place Local Agenda 21 strategies by the year 2000. Joint guidance issued by the Government, the Local Government Association and the Local Government

Management Board provides a checklist for local authorities working towards sustainable communities[15]:

◆ **A sustainable society seeks to :**

protect and enhance the environment:

- use energy, water and other natural resources efficiently and with care
- minimise waste, then re-use or recover it through recycling, composting or energy recovery, and finally sustainably dispose of what is left
- limit pollution to levels which do not damage natural systems
- value and protect the diversity of nature

meet social needs:

- create or enhance places, spaces and buildings that work well, wear well and look well
- make settlements "human" in scale and form
- value and protect diversity and local distinctiveness and strengthen local community and cultural identity
- protect human health and amenity through safe, clean, pleasant environments
- emphasise health service prevention action as well as care
- ensure access to good food, water, housing and fuel at reasonable cost
- meet local needs locally wherever possible
- maximise everyone's access to the skills and knowledge needed to play a full part in society
- empower all sections of the community to participate in decision-making and consider the social and community impacts of decisions

promote economic success:

- create a vibrant local economy that gives access to satisfying and rewarding work without damaging the local, national or global environment
- value unpaid work
- encourage necessary access to facilities, services, goods and other people in ways which make less use of the car and minimise impacts on the environment
- make opportunities for culture, leisure and recreation readily available to all

Adapted from LGMB 1994 The Sustainability Indicators Research Project

It is encouraging to see an emphasis on a positive concept of health, and the role of preventive health interventions. This should not be surprising given the established track record of many local authorities in the field of health promotion[16], but is still not fully recognised by some within the NHS.

Local Agenda 21 has been received with enthusiasm in many local government settings, and has formed the basis for some innovative joint working between health and local authorities[17]. However, the difficulties of establishing effective partnerships across sectoral boundaries are all too well known. Whilst some continue to regard LA21 and the supposedly complementary Health for All strategy as affording exciting opportunities, outside these areas concern remains about the extent to which the strategy forms a basis for health and local government to come together with communities to address specific health issues[18].

Sustainable development

The Government is currently developing a revised sustainable development strategy. The consultation paper relating to this strategy, *Opportunities for Change,* explicitly recognised the relationship between sustainability and health and made mention of the *Our Healthier Nation Strategy.* The consultation document identified a number of environmental factors which influence wellbeing and quality of life[19]:

- good air quality
- safe, secure and good quality housing
- safe drinking water
- access to open spaces
- proper use of chemicals and potentially hazardous substances.

These factors have now been distilled into a proposed set of headline sustainability indicators, intended to assist the Government in assessing the environmental impact of all their policies. In addition to the headline indicators, a set of around 150 more detailed indictors will be developed. The indicators are grouped under three objectives: the maintenance of high and stable levels of economic growth and employment; effective protection of the environment; and the prudent use of natural resources[20].

A number of the indicators have relevance to traditional public health concerns, such as water supply, sewerage and waste disposal services. However, the indicators also share a number of points in common with the new public health agenda, such as inequalities in health, employment, education and training, and housing quality. But the opportunity to make explicit the links between the environment and health has not been followed through: where health is referred to, the concern is with health *services* such as hospital buildings. This failure to recognise the range of influences that the environment has on health represents a major obstacle to effective partnership working, and reinforces the traditional roles of Government departments such as Environment and Health. The chosen indicators say little about the value of public participation, which is not only surprising given the importance placed on this in strategies such as LA21, but disappointing given the health benefits of a sense of empowerment and self-efficacy. The headline indicator which refers specifically to health does emphasise the difference in life expectancy between men in manual occupations and their professional counterparts, and signals further work on identifying healthy life expectancies which hopefully will take place in tandem with moves to reduce health inequalities. Finally, the indicators chosen for air pollution and transport have clear relevance for the neighbourhood setting, with air quality and road safety causing growing concern in particular neighbourhoods, often in more deprived parts of urban locations.

Regeneration

Much of the policy debate around neighbourhoods that has taken place in other policy spheres has concerned the processes of regeneration and renewal. This information is mainly useful in terms of what it says about *un*healthy neighbourhoods, how improvements have been achieved, and how opportunities have been lost. Concern has been escalating for some time that, despite considerable levels of investment in localised areas, many established regeneration programmes were failing to deliver value, either in terms of social capital or in terms of value for money. This has been one of the first issues to be considered by the Social Exclusion Unit.

Bringing Britain Together

In September 1998 the Social Exclusion Unit published a major report entitled *Bringing Britain Together: a national strategy for neighbourhood renewal.*[21] In their attempts to define a "poor neighbourhood" the SEU identified a number of factors associated with housing and the surrounding material and social environment which are known to be detrimental to health.

The connections between unemployment, poverty, poor housing and poor health are set out in *Bringing Britain Together*, along with the impact of inadequate primary health care services and the problems of accessing health care in deprived areas.[22]

The report signalled a new, three pronged approach to tackling the problems of poor neighbourhoods. The New Deal strategies for the unemployed, lone parents and the disabled are expected to play a central role in establishing a "virtuous cycle" of regeneration, in combination with new initiatives in education and crime reduction. The second element of the Government's strategy is a new initiative, the New Deal for Communities, intended to bring about effective regeneration but also to ensure that lessons are learned and good practice in this field is spread to other areas (see below). The third element of the strategy involves the establishment of 18 "cross-cutting action teams", which will each address problematic policy areas with the aim of securing collaboration between different agencies and departments to bring about new ways of addressing the seemingly intractable problems associated with poor neighbourhoods.

The teams are grouped under 5 thematic headings, one of which – "Getting the place to work" – has particular relevance for the healthy neighbourhood setting. The teams are as follows:

♦ **Action teams on social exclusion**

Getting the people to work

1. Jobs
2. Skills
3. Business

Getting the place to work

4. Neighbourhood management
5. Housing management
6. Neighbourhood wardens
7. Unpopular housing
8. Anti-social behaviour
9. Community self-help
10. Arts and sport

Building a future for young people:

11. Schools plus
12. Young people

Access to services:

13. Shops
14. Financial services
15. Information technology

Making the Government and Whitehall work better:

16 Learning lessons
17. Joining it up locally
18. Better information

Source: *Bringing Britain Together*

The New Deal for Communities

The New Deal for Communities is the first major output of the work of the Social Exclusion Unit. Announced as part of the Comprehensive Spending review, the New Deal constitutes a fund of £800 million over three years, made available to 17 pilot or "pathfinder" areas. The fund is to be used to address severe interrelated problems affecting these areas. The New Deal is based firmly on a geographical notion of community:

> The New Deal for Communities will be neighbourhood based. It does not matter whether the homes are owned by the local authority, by a housing association, privately rented, or owner occupied, so long as they form a recognisable neighbourhood[23]

The list of problems identified by the social exclusion unit perhaps serves as a definition of what a healthy neighbourhood is not - an area characterised by: poor job prospects; high levels of crime; a rundown environment; and no one in charge of managing the neighbourhood and co-ordinating the public services that affect it. The aim of the New Deal is to improve job prospects, bring together investment in buildings and investment in people, and to improve neighbourhood management and the delivery of services. There is a requirement on pathfinder applicants to develop their proposals in conjunction with local people, and an emphasis on securing the support and involvement of local communities. The lead agencies for the New Deal need not be local government, and housing associations and schools have been proposed as possible bodies to assume the lead in this new approach. The New Deal for Communities also recognises the need to work with the grain of other initiatives which may impact on the same area. Although the guidance paper mentions Employment and Health Action Zones, it is presumably also possible that a New Deal pathfinder site may come to incorporate a healthy neighbourhood setting.

The New Deal for Communities anticipates that proposals will seek to address all or some of the following areas:

◆ **New Deal Objectives**
- promoting employment
- promoting education and lifelong learning
- improving housing
- reducing crime and disorder
- providing for better neighbourhood management
- reducing problems associated with drugs misuse
- supporting families and young people, particularly children
- improving health
- building the community
- improving transport
- improving access to local services
- encouraging enterprise

Source: *Bringing Britain Together*

The guidance for pathfinder applicants refers to the need to improve access to primary and preventative health services with the aim of improving physical and mental health and reducing health inequalities. It is envisaged that this will be delivered through health promotion and education, possibly in the context of a Health Action Zone. However, although there are three social exclusion action teams addressing issues of access to services, access to health services does not form a part of their brief.

Supporting Families

The recently published consultation document *Supporting Families*[24] is concerned with issues affecting quality of life for parents and children, which are seen as central to the regeneration of deprived areas and communities. The document locates families firmly in the context of the community or neighbourhood, and sets out a principle aim of "strengthening the ways in which the wider family and communities support and nurture family life"[25].The document identifies a number of issues – access to support services, levels of income, family friendly employment - which have considerable influence over how healthy not just a family but a whole neighbourhood can be. *Supporting Families* proposes a number of new initiatives. The most relevant to the healthy neighbourhood setting are the Sure Start programme, as well as proposals to enhance the role of the health visitor, and plans to involve older members of the community in mentoring or supporting parents and young children.

Sure Start has a strong neighbourhood focus, with each programme serving the local community "within 'pram pushing' distance"[26]. The Sure Start programme is to be targeted on children and families in deprived circumstances. The programme is intended to be fully integrated into related initiatives, particularly the New Deal for Communities. With funding of £540 million over the first three years already announced, the initiative will be delivered through local partnerships (the precise nature of which has yet to be determined) with the aim of delivering a range of support services, including childcare, early learning and play opportunities, and support with parenting skills, as well as improved access to primary health care.

A number of the measures suggested in *Supporting Families* relate to the proposals for a national childcare strategy set out in the Green Paper *Meeting the Childcare Challenge*[27]. The strategy aims to ensure that appropriate childcare is available for children aged 0 to 14 in every neighbourhood. The strategy has three key aims: raising the quality of care; making childcare affordable; and making childcare more accessible by increasing places and improving information.

Supporting Families also floats a number of suggestions about the ways in which the traditional role of the health visitor could be enhanced, to meet the needs of families more closely. The proposals centre on changing the emphasis of health visiting work away from routine developmental screening, towards a more flexible focus on the individual needs of children and families. Health visitors do have the potential to be a key professional within the healthy neighbourhood setting. Many health visitors already carry case loads based on a neighbourhood or "patch" basis, and have a range of contacts with voluntary and statutory agencies that is almost unique in the primary care setting. In many respects, health visitors emerge as the natural candidate for the position of lynch-pin professional within the healthy neighbourhood setting. A number of the healthy neighbourhood initiatives featured below reported that they (and some of their health visiting colleagues) would welcome greater freedom to respond to local needs. However, many health visiting duties at present are determined either by statute or by rigid contractual arrangements. Health visitors receive specialist training, and have a clearly defined body of professional knowledge. This means that fundamental changes to their role are unlikely to be swiftly achievable: the process of reform will need to start without delay.

Supporting Families also makes a number of clear links between related settings, namely the family home, the wider neighbourhood, and the school or workplace. Schools in particular are seen as having the potential to become a resource not just for children but for the wider community. For example, proposals for the Family Literacy Initiative include a role for local schools in running literacy skills sessions jointly for both parents and children. Schools are also seen as providing a setting for involving older people in helping children to learn. And *Supporting Families* welcomes volunteering initiatives such as "step-grandparenting" which offer support for individual children or whole families. Schemes such as these will require careful and sensitive development if they are to achieve their potential, but the proposals in *Supporting Families* do at least show how links could be established between important and potentially healthy settings.

Regeneration, housing and health

Regeneration initiatives have frequently been criticised for failing to provide evidence of the impact of the initiative on the residents of an area. This has been particularly so in relation to the health impact of such initiatives: although the links between health and housing for instance can be hard to measure, in many cases there has been no attempt to measure health at all. There is however a body of evidence which does provide evidence of the links between poor neighbourhoods and health. It is worth reflecting that not only does a failure to fully consider and record the health impact of regeneration schemes mean that opportunities to learn from experience are missed, but that Government looses the opportunity to claim credit for health gains achieved along the way.

A review of the literature concerning housing and health conducted by Ambrose, Barlow et. al. reveals some striking findings[28]. Ambrose's own report on the "Health Gain" study he directed in Stepney concludes that there are no simple cause and effect relationships between health and housing: the picture is actually much more complicated [29]. For instance, Ambrose highlights the way that an individual's health may affect their income, and by extension their access to quality housing. Similarly, joblessness or job loss may result in poor mental health, and also potentially family breakdown, which again has implications not just for housing, but for the health of the neighbourhood as a whole.[30] The review highlights the links between poor housing and crime, as well as the effects on educational attainment. Carr-Hill et al. found that people housed in poor conditions consumed 50% more health services than would otherwise be expected[31]. Similarly, exploratory work by Barrow and Brachan[32] found that annual health costs at £515 per household in poor housing in Stepney compared to £72 per household in improved housing in Paddington – a difference by a factor of about seven.

Health is further linked to housing quality through factors such as dampness, which is associated with high levels of diseases such as asthma[33], the adequacy of heating, and safety features which lead, for example, to people living in high rise accommodation suffering the highest levels of serious household injury, including falls[34].

A series of criteria for identifying housing of a satisfactory quality has been provided by The Cost Effectiveness in Housing Investment Programme, and is attached as Appendix two.

Past regeneration initiatives have been criticised for failing to involve residents adequately in the decision making process, or even keeping them informed of decisions made[35]. Participation, and the importance of feeling a sense of control and influence over events affecting day to day life, have been linked firmly to health and well being. Peter Ambrose's research observes that a sense of disempowerment can have profound effects on individuals' coping resources, and highlights the contribution to poor physical and mental health made by years of neglect of housing stock.[36] The ability to involve neighbourhood residents in the development of a healthy neighbourhood programme will be central to the success of this strategy. It is encouraging that the importance of this crucial element has been recognised[37]. However, for the contribution of local people to be fully realised will require an investment in terms of both time and capacity.

This body of evidence clearly suggests that the quality of the physical neighbourhood – individual homes and shared surroundings – has a very real impact on health, and points toward it forming a legitimate focus for health improvement in the healthy neighbourhood setting. So, having considered the policy framework, and the evidence about the factors that make a neighbourhood healthy or otherwise, what are the practical approaches that will be instrumental in improving health on the ground?

Community Resources

The success of strategies and initiatives aimed at developing healthy neighbourhoods will depend to a very large extent on the ways in which neighbourhood projects involve local people in identifying problems and solutions, to shape and deliver action for health gain. This section considers some approaches which aim to work with local communities to build social networks and capacity. Healthy neighbourhood projects will need to work with local people and redress, complement or supplement the community resources already in place.

Community Development

The term "community development" sums up an approach to working with communities that places the development of the skills and capacities of local people at its heart. Community development represents a rather diverse movement, which can make precise definitions difficult. As well as an established track record working in the field of health, the community development approach has spanned a number of different subjects ranging from single issue concerns, such as local road safety, to broader thematic concerns such as community participation by people from ethnic minorities. It has been suggested that Healthy Living Centres, and by extension healthy neighbourhoods, will need to be informed by a community development perspective[38]. And there is no doubt that it is the ideas and experiences of community development in its broad sense which will inform the development of the healthy neighbourhood setting.

One particularly influential model is that of the Pioneer Health Centre, which operated in Peckham 1935 and 1950 [39]. Designed as an "experiment in social medicine", the centre emphasised the need to work with "whole groups" – families and communities – in order to promote health and wellbeing. The Centre pioneered the notion of "pram pushing distance" now adopted by Sure Start and other initiatives, ensuring that the Centre was easily accessible to all members of the family. Housed in purpose built premises, the Centre offered a range of facilities including a swimming pool and gymnasium. It had a cafeteria, which used largely organic produce from the Centre's other site, a farm in Bromley Common. And the social facilities and nursery provided by the Centre were highly valued by the local residents who used it. The Peckham Experiment has continued to be influential even after its closure, and has been credited with informing the development of contemporary Healthy Living Centres.

Healthy Living Centres

The Government has announced that a network of Healthy Living Centres is to be established. £300 million of Lottery funding will be distributed to Healthy Living Centres throughout the UK by the New Opportunities Fund with the aim of ensuring that around 20% of the population has access to a centre.[40] In addition to the financial support provided NOF, the centres will be expected to find a proportion of their funding through partnership arrangements.

The Healthy Living Centres concept is tied closely to the Government's strategy for public health, and in particular the reduction of inequalities in health. In announcing Healthy Living Centres, the Department of Health stated:

> *Healthy Living Centres will address locally identified health needs and contribute to the achievement of local health strategies and targets which will reflect the very wide range of issues which contribute to health and wellbeing. Priority will be given to projects which focus on areas of deprivation, urban and rural, and the needs of people who experience worse needs than average.*[41]

Although the guidance for pilot centres stresses the need for flexibility and innovation in developing the concept, six general principles have been identified which underpin the Healthy Living Centre concept, namely:

- a clear link with the new public health strategy, and an emphasis on tackling local health inequalities
- the adoption of a community development approach, and sensitivity to local circumstances
- the creation of innovative partnerships across the voluntary, private and public sectors
- ensuring that development is complementary to English Health Action Zones
- securing funding that will enable the project to be sustained after the Lottery funding ends
- demonstrating additionality: the services funded by NOF must not supplant services provided through core funding[42]

Each Health Action Zone will be expected to incorporate at least one Healthy Living Centre, as they are viewed by the Government as an essential element of regeneration.[43] Outside HAZs, some healthy neighbourhoods too will include a Healthy Living Centre. But a Healthy Living Centre is not an essential ingredient of a healthy neighbourhood. Neighbourhoods will need to decide what sort of facilities and action will best suit their circumstances.

Summary

A strategy to promote healthy neighbourhoods faces the challenge of drawing together a considerable range of related policies and initiatives which have a part to play in improving quality of life, health and wellbeing. This task is further complicated by the fact that too often these various initiatives fail to fully recognise the impact their actions have or could have on the health of local people. The healthy neighbourhood setting could provide a policy focus which would raise awareness of these issues, helping to ensure that policy across a number of spheres is better co-ordinated, and that health gains are maximised.

References

[14] A. Scriven and S. Young, "Health promotion, Environmental Health and Agenda 21", *Journal of the Royal Society of Health*, April 1998, 118; 2, 85-90

[15] Department of the Environment, Transport and the Regions, *Sustainable Local Communities for the 21st Century: Why and how to prepare an effective local agenda 21 strategy,* February 1998

[16] See for example Health Education Authority with the Local Governmnet Association, *Health on the Agenda? A guide to health strategy development for local authorities*, London, HEA, 1997

[17] A number of examples are included in *Sustainable Local Communities, op.cit.*

[18] See for example A. Scriven and S. Young, *Health Promotion, op. cit.*

[19] Department of the Environment, Transport and the Regions, *Sustainable Local Communities for the 21st Century, op.cit*

[20] Source: Department of Transport, Environment and the Regions, *Sustainability Counts*, November 1998

[21] The Social Exclusion Unit, *Bringing Britain Together, ibid.*

[22] The Social Exclusion Unit, *Bringing Britain Together: a national strategy for neighbourhood renewal*, HMSO, Cm 4045, September 1998

[23] Department of Transport, Environment and the Regions, *New Deal for Communities, Phase 1 Proposals: Guidance for Applicants*, 15th September 1998

[24] Home Office, *Supporting Families: A consultation document,* The Stationery Office, London, 1998.

[25] Home Office, *Supporting Families, ibid.*

[26] Home Office, *Supporting Families, ibid.*

[27] Department for Education and Employment, *Meeting the Childcare Challenge*, The Stationery Office, London, May, 1998.

[28] P. Ambrose, Barlow J. et.al., *The Real Cost of Poor Homes*, Royal Institute of Chartered Surveyors, 1996

[29] P. Ambrose, *I Mustn't Laugh Too Much: Housing and Health on the Limehouse Fields and Ocean Estates in Stepney*, Centre for Urban and Regional Research, University of Sussex, 1996

[30] Ambrose, *I mustn't laugh too much, ibid,* p12.

[31] R.Carr-Hill, D.Coyle and C.Ivens, *Poor Housing: Poor Health?*, Unpublished report funded by the Department of the Environment, London, 1993, cited in Ambrose et.al., *Bad Housing, ibid.*

[32] M. Barrow and R. Bachan, 1997, *The Real Cost of Poor Homes: Footing the Bill*, Royal Institute of Chartered Surveyors

[33] L.Arblaster, M.Hawtin, "Health, housing and social policy", Socialist Health Association, 1993, cited in *Report of the Independent Inquiry into Inequalities in Health,* ibid

[34] R.Best, "The Housing Dimension", in Bezeval, Judge and Whitehead, eds. "Tackling inequalities in health: an agenda for action", The King's Fund, 1995, cited in the *Report of the Independent Inquiry, op.cit.*

[35] Social Exclusion Unit, *Bringing Britain Together, op.cit.*

[36] P. Ambrose, *I Mustn't Laugh Too Much, op.cit.*

[37] Speech by Tessa Jowell, Minister of State for Public Health, reported in Department of Health, 1998, *Healthy Living Centres: Report of a seminar held on 2nd April 1998*

[38] Speech by Tessa Jowell, Minister of State for Public Health, reported in Department of Health, 1998, *Healthy Living Centres: Report of a seminar held on 2nd April 1998*

[39] A. Stallibrass, *Being Me and Also Us: Lessons from the Peckham experiment*, Scottish Academic Press, Edinburgh, 1989

[40] Department of Health Circular dated 3rd July 1998

[41] Department of Health Circular dated 30th December 1997

[42] Source: health service circular dated 30th December 1997, op.cit

[43] Department of Health, *Healthy Living Centres*, Report of a seminar held on 2nd April 1998, ibid

Section Four: Healthy neighbourhoods in action

The neighbourhood setting doesn't only form a focus for policy. Increasingly, local people and organisations around the country are realising the potential of action at neighbourhood level to improve the health of the people who live there. This section outlines five neighbourhood based initiatives which are working to improve the health and wellbeing of communities. The projects chosen offer contrasting approaches to developing a healthy neighbourhood, but each show what could be achieved around the country given the support of Government and local agencies. Coverage of each of the five initiatives opens with a brief description. Four key aspects of the projects are then considered in relation to the following questions:

- How has the project identified its neighbourhood?
- What are the principle objectives of the project, and how do they reflect local concerns?
- What activities is the project undertaking?
- How will the project be taking its work forward?

The Beckton Community Health Project

Overview: The Beckton Community Health Project involves residents from all sections of the community in a range of local activities aimed at improving the health of their neighbourhood. The project began in 1993/4, with input from East London and the City Health Authority, the London Docklands Development Corporation, Sheffield University and the King's Fund Grants Committee.

The neighbourhood: The neighbourhood served by the project is larger than might be found elsewhere, but forms a readily identifiable geographical entity on the ground. The neighbourhood of Beckton is bordered on one side by the London docks, and on the other sides by major roads. The rapid development part-funded by LDDC in the 1980s saw Beckton's population quadruple from 5,000 to it's current level of around 20,000 people. The area consists almost entirely residential housing, and there is a marked lack of amenities. The absence of small local shops is particularly striking, with a large supermarket forming the focal point of what had originally been designed as the "district centre". Despite 1 in 3 of the population being aged 0 to 19, there is a similar underprovision of schools in the area, with no secondary school at all. 80% of Beckton's residents are registered with one large GP practice. Although the housing was originally built for owner-occupation, the subsequent collapse of the housing market and resulting repossessions led to housing associations buying up the stock in bulk. As well as indigenous Eastenders the area now houses a large number of people from ethnic minorities, including many asylum seekers and refugees accepted from the local authority's housing waiting list.

Objectives: The Beckton Community Health Project aims to "promote wellbeing through reducing stress levels, depression, social isolation and to empower local communities to make healthy lifestyle choices for themselves and their children"[44]. The project uses a community development approach, and the views and resources of local people are central to the action it undertakes. A consultation exercise called "Your Shout" was conducted by local people themselves, and has enabled residents to have their say about how the quality of life for people in Beckton could be improved. Local people take a very broad view of the factors that affect their health and wellbeing, and this is reflected in the range of activities that the project is involved in.

Action: Based in a local community centre, the project is co-ordinated by the former director of the centre and employs one full time development worker. The Beckton Community Health Project works very closely with local residents in planning and carrying out work. A committee comprising local residents and professional staff meets regularly to monitor progress and make decisions about future events. Activities undertaken so far include working with local people to clear and renovate a pond and garden area, creating an attractive area for local people to use and relax in. A separate project has involved children in designing and making beautiful mosaic inlaid benches and paving to surround the pond area. These initiatives address one of the over-riding problems for the neighbourhood – the lack of amenities for local people to use and enjoy. Other volunteers, together with the development worker, have been taking part in sessions with young people where they discuss – often heatedly – health issues such as drug use, sexual health and domestic violence. This approach is proving popular with younger residents, who enjoy passing on and receiving this knowledge and information.

The future: Work on the pond and mosaic projects is continuing. The project hopes to continue to establish Action Groups around additional issues of concern to local people, to complement the focus already established on youth and older people's issues. Efforts are being made to establish a health forum, in partnership with local primary care services.

The "Looking Well" Centre, Bentham, North Yorkshire[45]

Overview: The Looking Well Centre was established in response to a community consultation exercise called "Getting Together" carried out in 1995 by local agencies in response to the previous Government's Local Voices initiative. The Looking Well centre is a community centre which uses creative arts projects to promote community development. The Centre has a homely feel, with a wood burning stove at its heart, and aims to provide a congenial space with the atmosphere of an extended family. The experiences of the project have lead those involved to conclude that involvement in creative activities can benefit health.

The neighbourhood: The market town of Bentham is on the borders of three counties; North Yorkshire, Lancashire and Cumbria. It has a population of around 3,000. Although the town occupies an attractive rural setting near to the Lake District, life for the residents can be far from idyllic. Its position at the margins of three counties sometimes contributes to a climate of isolation. Facilities such as social services and other council offices are some distance away, and difficult to reach without access to a car. Employment in the town is predominantly within the troubled farming industry, or within local small industries and shops.

Objectives: The aims of the Looking Well Centre were influenced by the findings of "Getting Together" which identified high levels of depression, loneliness and isolation. The project is targeted at the whole population of Bentham, especially those at risk of poor mental health. The project aims to enhance emotional and mental wellbeing by providing a safe environment in which people can come together to give and receive support, and by facilitating opportunities for people to share skills and knowledge and be creative. The Centre has been designed to provide a community-led workspace in which creative activities can take place, and also provides an attractive and welcoming meeting place. The Centre is used by local residents of all ages, and also has visitors from surrounding towns and villages. Over 400 people used the Centre in the six months to April 1998.

Action: Arts based activities have included public lantern making workshops and a lantern procession through the town. Flags, banners and model birds have also been created and displayed around the town. Involvement with the Centre has also led local people to develop their own responses to specific issues. Users have helped to organise groups to tackle issues including domestic violence and young people's health, either on their own initiative or together with local organisations. Other activities taking place at the Centre include the Mucky Buckets play project, which unlike many traditional nurseries encourages parents and children to play together, and a local exchange trading scheme (LETS).

Management of the Centre is overseen by a project director and the board of trustees including arts and health professionals from the Pioneer Projects board, a registered charity established by local partner agencies to administer the Centre. Day to day management is carried out by a committee of volunteers who either use the Centre themselves or represent particular user groups.

The future: Evaluation of the project is ongoing, with support from a King's Fund development grant. Future plans include the possibility of providing a certificate in adult education through the Centre. The next stage of project development will be taking place under the banner of Bentham Healthy Community, and will seek to expand the work already undertaken beyond the Centre.

Matson Neighbourhood Project, Gloucester

Overview: The Matson Neighbourhood Project is part of a network of eight neighbourhood based projects in operation throughout Gloucestershire. Each of the neighbourhood project areas in the network has a concentration of social housing at its heart and has been developed as a peripheral urban estate or town.

The neighbourhood: The community of Matson is in the south of Gloucester, near to the M5. Matson is about 4 miles from Gloucester city centre, but is separated from the city by open countryside. The area contains one of the largest council estates in Gloucester, as well as a small quantity of private housing. A few very high quality private residences border the northern side of the village, again backing on to open countryside. The estate is home to approximately 8,000 people. The population is mixed in terms of age, and contains very few people from ethnic minorities. The principal sources of employment for residents are found in retail and light industry in Gloucester itself. Unemplyemnt is around 12%.

Objectives: The project is run by local people for local people. It aims to generate a new and enduring social infrastructure by combining community lead services with local statutory and business interests. The project is concerned to ensure effective local co-ordination and delivery of primary health as well as a range of other caring services. The project was the first organisation to open any kind of office on the estate.

Action: The project focuses its work around the linked themes of community health, community education and community enterprise, and delivers activities through four teams: advice and representation; jobs and training; mental health and learning disabilities; and economic and community development. The project team consists of a combination of around 30 paid and volunteer staff, who are local residents.

The project operates from four main premises around the neighbourhood. The Trinity Centre - formerly a disused Co-op shop – has been cited as a model of a small healthy living centre. It combines the estate's only GP surgery with an advice centre, a community shop and an IT learning centre. It also offers a number of caring and support services, including home delivery shopping, debt counselling, marriage guidance, chiropody and even hairdressing. Around 3,000 people used the project's telephone and face to face advisory services last year.

The project's One Stop Shop is located next to the council's housing office on the small parade of shops in the middle of the estate. This centre offers another advice centre and information and support concerning jobs and training, as well as selling second hand clothes. The third project location is on nearby Matson Lane which houses the Phoenix Club. Project members facilitate a drop in centre providing a service three days a week to people with mental health problems and learning difficulties. This centre involves 75 residents, and has an average attendance of 25.

At Matson Baptist Church the project has a flexible learning centre which delivers some of the project's education programmes, including courses aimed at promoting health and wellbeing such as confidence building, parenting and fostering and food handling.

Other services and activities provided by various elements of the project include an after-school children's club, a family centre and crèche used by people attending courses, a lunch club and taxi service for the over 60s and a carers forum which meets monthly. Referrals to the project can be made by all local health and social services staff, using a simple tick box form provided by the project.

Residents can stand for election to the Management Committee at the annual general meeting, and can also be co-opted to serve on it throughout the year. There are also subcommittees which deal with financial and building issues, personnel and local projects. The project is administered by a Board, again comprised of local people or people with a strong connection to the area, who are not paid employees of the project. Any Matson resident can join the project free of charge. Core funding is supplied by Gloucester County Council, with additional funding for specific projects from a National Lottery grant and local charities, as well as various commercial sponsors.

The future: The project is currently considering the feasibility of introducing a credit union in the area. Another emerging local priority concerns neighbourhood management, and project members are in discussion with the council about greater involvement of residents in planning and perhaps providing this service. The project is also involved in developing a community foyer which would provide accommodation for 32 people and is intended to support divided families and young people leaving home. The project has grown and changed considerably since its inception, and is now moving towards offering its volunteers formal opportunities for personal development in areas like interview skills. It is also developing international partnerships with neighbourhoods in other countries.

The St Matthew's Project, Leicester

Overview: The St. Matthew's project is based in a deprived council housing estate in Leicester. The project is multi-faceted, and hinges around a multi-disciplinary centre which delivers a range of services aimed at improving the quality of life for residents on the estate and providing teaching opportunities to equip professionals to manage society's medical problems.

The neighbourhood: The St. Matthew's estate is home to about 4,500 people. The area was first developed as part of a slum clearance programme in the 1950's and has since grown to incorporate a mixture of low and high rise buildings which are now in a generally poor state of repair. The estate is bordered by major roads, and has a distinct local identity. Incomes of residents are exceptionally low, with high unemployment and resultant deprivation. The area has high levels of crime (including violent street crime) and drug use. The population is quite transient, with half the lettings reallocated yearly. This partially stems from the local authority's use of readily available vacant stock to house refugees – the estate recently received 500 evacuees from Montserrat – but also reflects the determination of many residents to move off the estate.

Objectives: The project aims to improve the health of residents of the St Matthew's estate by addressing issues that have been identified as local needs and priorities by the residents themselves. It also plays an important role in educating health and social care professionals about the needs of deprived communities, and has pioneered new approaches to professional training.

Action: The St. Matthew's project is the result of co-ordinated efforts by a number of local agencies, spearheaded by a local GP. Before the project started there were inadequate primary health care facilities located within the estate. Residents' health was poor, but the pressures of their living conditions meant that seeking out primary care was low on their list of concerns. Consultation with local people established that the most pressing needs as they perceived them were somewhere for children to play, and a safe place for women to relax and socialise. As well as an attractive and welcoming coffee bar and children's play area, Prince Philip

House (a multi-disciplinary health and community centre established by the project) also provides a range of health care facilities, including a GP surgery and dental services. The community rooms on the ground floor of the centre are now heavily utilised, accommodating regular visits from a private optician, as well as sessions held by a solicitor and a domestic violence project. Some of the services located in Prince Philip House have a community wide focus, such as the Police Office, and the financial contribution secured by their presence helps the viability of the project. Others are specifically targeted at residents of the estate, including community mental health services and a drugs and alcohol project. The centre also houses a University of Leicester academic base to oversee the growing programme of professional training. Fosse Health (NHS) Community Trust, the key partner in Prince Philip House, relocated therapy services into the building to develop a business case and ensure financial security.

The project is co-ordinated by an area forum, which brings together professional and managerial staff from the public sector and voluntary bodies operating in the neighbourhood. Public involvement in the forum is achieved by having the ward councillor act as Chair. The emphasis on involving staff working in the area is carried through into the second tier of the project's organisational structure, in the shape of sub-groups which deal with three key issues of local concern: economic regeneration, children and young people's support, and community safety. The professionals in these groups are charged with working with residents to translate local priorities into a plan of action to resolve identified problems. The area forum links with Leicester-wide policy makers to work together to reduce disadvantage.

The future: The project is currently involved in setting up an initiative to improve the economic basis of the neighbourhood, through better training and employment opportunities. The project already benefits from having a secondee from Marks and Spencer working on the team, with the aim of developing a business strategy to ensure the project is sustainable in the long term and not dependent on one or two key individuals. The project also works with Business-in-the-Community to help develop individual initiatives. The project is undergoing a 3 year evaluation exercise, part funded by the NHS Executive. The outcome of this study will influence the evolution of the emerging model of multi-agency service provision and professional training.

Bradford: Gardening for health[46] [47]

Overview: The Gardening for Health project is a partnership between Heartsmart (a branch of Bradford District Health Promotion Service), the Bradford Community Environment Project, and local women from the Bangladeshi community. The project developed from a series of consultation and community meetings with the women. Many women in the Bangladeshi community spend a great deal of time in their home. Opportunities for physical exercise are very limited through a combination of cultural and practical factors. The idea of a community gardening project seemed to meet a lot of the women's needs at once: it provides an opportunity for the women to grow food, talk and learn about healthy eating, and involves plenty of physical exercise and social interaction within an environment that is culturally appropriate.

The neighbourhood: There is a well established community of about 7,000 people of Bangladeshi origin living in Bradford, following a period of immigration which began in the late 1950s. Most members of the community are Muslim, and Sylheti is the main spoken language. Around half of the adults in the community do not read, speak or write English. As well as being a community of interest, the Bangledeshi community is also centred on four particular districts in Bradford. Most people within the community live in privately owned older terraced houses, many of which are in a state of disrepair. There is considerable pressure on accommodation resulting in part from the extended family structure which prevails, and overcrowding is a feature of many households. There are high levels of unemployment within the community, which was badly affected by the collapse of the textile market. The community experiences high levels of deprivation and health inequalities, particularly in relation to heart disease.

Objectives: The project was approached from a community development perspective. The emphasis has been on local people identifying issues that should be addressed, and then working with them to help them develop the skills and resources to do so. The project set out to benefit the women through the promotion of physical activity and healthy eating, plus developing new skills and self confidence. It also had an environmental focus, promoting recycling and the consumption of locally produced organic food. And it benefited the wider community, by developing local action and decision making, and by regenerating a derelict allotment site.

Action: The women involved, who are mainly aged 35 and over, have received basic training in gardening which supplemented the knowledge some of the women had already developed through cultivating plots of land in Bangladesh. The women came for sessions on the allotments on four days a week, for two hours at a time. Transport to and from the site was provided. The first harvest in 1997 included onions, cabbages, fenugreek, beans, tomatoes, courgettes, radishes, coriander, blackberries and raspberries. Traditional Bangladeshi vegetables suited to the British climate were also grown, including mooli radishes, a leafy vegetable called duggi, and Khudu pumpkins. Over time the physical health of the women has been seen to improve, and their increasing stamina is enabling some to take part in longer sessions. Project workers also report improved mental health among the women, who have gained self-esteem and seem less prone to depression.

The future: The project is continuing, with the allotment bedded down and prepared as far as possible for planting to begin again in the spring.

Summary

The initiatives outlined above represent a range of approaches and arise out of different types of neighbourhoods. The models they offer vary from a service lead approach which has achieved significant progress within a highly deprived neighbourhood, to a strongly participatory "bottom up" approach. They are all able to point to significant progress, but this has been achieved over different time scales. Interestingly, none of them reported having experienced any difficulty in defining or identifying their neighbourhoods, which seem to have presented themselves quite naturally. All five are centred on communities of place, although the Gardening for Health project also involves a community of interest. They have all developed managerial and administrative structures, although each differs according to the approach of the project. And a common factor in all of them is that they started with a process of consultation, which enables them to reflect the broad ranging and far sighted approach which local people believe will improve their health.

References

[44] Beckton Community Health project, *Annual Review 1997/98*

[45] Sources: Health Education Authority, "Looking Well Centre (North Yorkshire)" *Community Action for Mental Health*, London, 1998

[46] Heartsmart report, *Gardening for Health in the Bradford District*, produced by Bradford District Health Promotion Service

[47] Source: Shell Better Britain Campaign Project Profile 33, *Gardening for Health*, May 1998

Section Five: Building healthy neighbourhoods

Developing healthy neighbourhoods

The inclusion of the neighbourhood setting in the Government's new strategy for public health could bring tremendous benefits to people whose health needs can sometimes be overlooked by traditional public health approaches. But the Government has not yet indicated how the neighbourhood setting will operate in conjunction with all the other area based policies and initiatives currently flooding out of Whitehall. Nor is it yet clear whether the neighbourhood setting will be developed in a way that enables it to bridge the gap in the *Our Healthier Nation* strategy, extending its coverage beyond schools and workplaces? In addition to the unresolved policy issues, another important question remains unanswered. Will Government and local agencies rise to the challenge of making healthy neighbourhoods a comprehensive, universal and *practical* initiative, building on the success of the healthy neighbourhoods featured in this report and extending the benefits to neighbourhoods all over the country?

This section considers these issues, and looks at how a policy framework that supports the development of an inclusive and effective healthy neighbourhood strategy could be achieved.

Although harder to define and less developed as a concept at present, the healthy neighbourhood setting needs to become as meaningful and robust as the school and workplace settings. For healthy neighbourhoods to become the unifying force of the *Our Healthier Nation Strategy*, rather than the weak link in the chain, everyone involved will need to be clear about what is being asked, and offered. We suggest:

◆ **A healthy neighbourhood is:**

- safe
- clean
- inclusive

- confident
- creative
- connected

In order to be meaningful, healthy neighbourhoods need to be defined by the people who live in them. And identifying a neighbourhood need not be an overly abstract process. Local people generally have little difficulty in describing the features and boundaries of their own neighbourhood. In practice, neighbourhoods often combine an element of geography – natural or man-made boundaries – with one or more communities of interest. They are a combination of people and places. But while local social networks and geographical boundaries may be broadly coterminous they will not always correspond to existing organisational structures, posing an additional challenge for local agencies. And, clearly, neighbourhoods contain both schools and workplaces. There is a clear case to be made for Government to define healthy neighbourhoods in terms of an overarching setting. This approach carries advantages at a practical local level, but could also enhance policy making in a range of related spheres – a theme which will be returned to below.

Healthy neighbourhoods will need to be grounded in local needs and priorities. Frequently the results of local consultation exercises, like those featured in section four, show that local people are aware of and attach most importance to the underlying determinants of ill-health. *Our Healthier Nation* recognises the importance of factors such as air quality, housing and the social environment[48]. These are the issues that tend to dominate local people's health concerns, sometimes against the expectations of health professionals. By working with the grain of local people's own health agenda, healthy neighbourhoods will stand to have a much greater impact on the factors that really do affect people's health and well being.

In starting this process, neighbourhoods will need to take stock of the resources that are available to them. Initiatives will need to identify, value and build on existing capacities and strengths.

♦ **A healthy neighbourhood has:**

- **Resources**: buildings, land, people
- **Knowledge**: experience of what is needed, and what will work
- **Amenities**, including sports and leisure facilities, attractive public spaces

- **Many components**: including **schools and workplaces**
- **Services**: private, public and voluntary bodies already on site
- **Potential**: assets and capacities that can develop to improve health

Healthy neighbourhood initiatives should not be seen principally in terms of service provision. To be effective, the approach will need to be about what neighbourhoods can offer, as well as what they need. For the most part, neighbourhoods will be able to offer the knowledge and enthusiasm of local people as well as their time and effort, although support may be required to unlock this potential. Neighbourhoods are unlikely to have substantial financial resources, or ready access to in depth information. They are likely to need support from a variety of sources to develop and sustain progress.

The appointment of development and support workers to work with local people, identifying and developing capacity and providing an interface with the private, public and voluntary sectors could greatly aid this process. Such staff could most efficiently be appointed to work across a whole district to support a number of neighbourhood projects or, exceptionally, to develop a project in just one particularly deprived neighbourhood. One function of such a post could be to manage a resource centre as an information and advice point on issues such as sources of funding or practical approaches to community projects. This role does not require the creation of a new profession, nor should it necessarily signal a return to the 1970s model of community development. It is possible, for instance, that some existing health, local government or voluntary sector personnel could be well equipped to fulfil such a role. So what kinds of people stand to benefit from healthy neighbourhoods initiatives?

♦ **A healthy neighbourhood should be for:**

- **everyone**, especially:
- young families
- older people
- people on low incomes
- people who are less mobile

Healthy neighbourhoods will have the greatest impact on health if they include all kinds of people in all kinds of places. As we have seen, neighbourhoods are seldom made up of homogenous groups of people. People whose mobility is restricted – through poverty, caring responsibilities, cultural factors, age or physical disability – are the people to whom the neighbourhood means most. Although geographical clustering of some of these groups is a feature, older people and people with disabilities or with caring responsibilities in particular are found in many different types of neighbourhoods. The possibility of directing healthy neighbourhoods initiatives exclusively towards neighbourhoods with the lowest incomes, although attractive on the face of it, should be resisted. Poverty and poor health are often concentrated in certain geographical areas, and local agencies will undoubtedly wish to make particular populations the focus of local action to reduce health inequalities. Healthy neighbourhoods initiatives may provide one very useful vehicle for bringing about such change. But an exclusive concentration on areas of high deprivation could lead to people who stand to make considerable health gains from healthy neighbourhoods missing out because of where they live. Healthy neighbourhood projects should focus on whole neighbourhoods of every kind, and then if necessary target specific groups within those neighbourhoods. Healthy neighbourhoods should be everyone's initiative.

♦ **Healthy neighbourhoods should be:**

- everywhere

Healthy schools and healthy workplaces are to be developed all around the country. Healthy neighbourhoods will need to be similarly comprehensive. Such an approach represents an opportunity to bring together many of the other existing area based initiatives currently taking shape around the country, giving cohesive force not just to public health but to a range of other Government policies. Instead of perceiving healthy neighbourhoods as just another initiative which must find ways of fitting alongside programmes like Sure Start and the New Deal for Communities, healthy neighbourhoods could form an overarching policy context within which other measures aimed at improving quality of life, health and well being are located. The Department of Health is already working with other Government departments and agencies to help them consider the health implications of their policies and actions. The healthy neighbourhoods setting could be used to underpin this process, providing a valuable focus for policy formulation and evaluation which is meaningful both in Whitehall and in neighbourhoods around the country.

There are other advantages to ensuring that anywhere that wishes can become a healthy neighbourhood. And there is a strong case to be made for any funding bodies avoiding complex competitive bidding procedures in identifying neighbourhoods to take forward the initiative. Healthy neighbourhoods will rely on the active involvement of local people for their success. An excessively detailed and bureaucratic application or registration procedure either at local or national level would risk the inception stage being dominated by organisations and professionals, rather than being informed and led by the views of local people. The emphasis should be on striving to become a healthier neighbourhood, rather than having to demonstrate what an unhealthy place it is to begin with. Healthy neighbourhood projects should embody a wide range of neighbourhoods and people - urban and rural, poor and affluent, and diverse in terms of culture, age and occupation. That way, lessons learned from early projects would have the widest possible applicability. And success stories will encourage more neighbourhoods to develop projects when they see the approach working in a place like their own.

A contract for healthy neighbourhoods

Although every community will bring a different approach to becoming a healthy neighbourhood, all areas will have some essential requirements in common. The contract for health set out in Our Healthier Nation provides a useful framework for considering the requirements each of the players will have, and the contributions they should make, if a strategy to develop healthy neighbourhoods is to work effectively.

In its present form the Government's new contract for health accommodates the school and workplace settings slightly more readily than the healthy neighbourhood. The difficulty stems from the descriptions of "local and community players" and "people" set out in the Green Paper. Local and community players are seen as organisations – whether public, private or voluntary. And the reference to people deals with individual lifestyle choices and actions. These distinctions are quite helpful in the other two settings, with the school and workplace fitting the organisational bill, and people being naturally defined in their roles as schoolchildren and employees. But within the healthy neighbourhood the boundaries between these two groups will be blurred. Successful initiatives will require the active participation of local people acting not just as individuals but as a community. And although local people will need to develop a degree of organisation in order to be effective, they will not necessarily coalesce into formalised "community players". It is important to recognise that a layer of organisation exists that lies between community organisations and individuals. This layer will be crucial for the successful development of healthy neighbourhoods, and needs a clear place in the contract for health.

For this reason, although the single term "neighbourhood" is used in adopting the model of the contract for health below, it is worth noting that it actually refers to all of the intermediate level players – including health and local authorities, professionals with an interest in the area, voluntary organisations, religious and community groups and, crucially, local people acting collectively - who will need to work together at local level to turn the strategy into action. It should also be remembered that schools and local businesses, as both employers and service providers, are important players within the neighbourhood setting. So, what should Government do?

◆ **Government could:**
  - provide guidance on making a healthy neighbourhood
  - identify and encourage those neighbourhoods where action is most needed
  - establish a support network and information exchange
  - acknowledge and reward effort and success

In launching the healthy neighbourhoods initiative, Government should aim to fulfil a pro-active, supportive role. Guidance about the scope of the initiative will be crucial in ensuring that the healthy neighbourhoods concept is meaningful to all the contract players, and will help to overcome any initial cynicism. Government needs to communicate to the organisations and individuals concerned exactly what they are being asked to sign up to, and how it can be turned to local advantage.

Government should also be concerned with promoting equity and inclusivity. Inevitably those neighbourhoods which have most to gain are likely to initiate action on their own behalf. Importantly, Government could require health and local authorities to take the necessary steps to ensure that deprived neighbourhoods are able to develop their own local projects . And new ways need to be found for Government to communicate directly with local people who might wish their neighbourhood to become involved. Innovative approaches like the road shows that have been used to launch Healthy Living Centres may be one way of doing this. Just as there are disadvantages associated with deliberately focusing exclusively on the most deprived areas, so there are risks associated with a healthy neighbourhoods strategy inadvertently attracting predominantly affluent communities. Government needs to reach out to neighbourhoods everywhere.

Politicians and other policy makers will need information about the impact of healthy neighbourhoods initiatives. Epidemiological data showing broad trends in health status that may be partially attributable to the initiative may not be available for some time. Information about local activities, process and outcomes will also be sought. And this type of information will not only be useful to Government - it will be invaluable to neighbourhood level players too, as they seek to develop and try new approaches. Government should oversee the establishment of a support network and the facilitation of an information exchange. As well as spreading examples of good practice and successful approaches, such a network could help to share information about practical evaluative techniques.

Finally, Government could take steps to acknowledge and reward successful healthy neighbourhoods. It has already been established that the healthy schools initiative is to have its own awards scheme, "Investors in Health". And a healthy workplaces award has been in existence for some time. Although a degree of cynicism and "award fatigue" is evident in some official circles, support for awards remains strong at the neighbourhood level and with local people. Administering an awards scheme for a nation wide initiative need not be too daunting a task. The "Investors in Health" award could be extended to cover neighbourhoods either individually or at district level, with areas that meet certain benchmark criteria receiving the award. Awards and official acknowledgement can raise the profile of a project by generating publicity which may attract wider support and draw new people into the project. However well local neighbourhood partnerships function, in some areas they will inevitably involve a number of people working in a voluntary capacity or undertaking activities on top of their core responsibilities. Projects like this depend on good will and sustained commitment. Building in opportunities to reflect on progress and celebrate successes can be important in maintaining enthusiasm, as well as a useful learning device. But as well as action at Governmental level, neighbourhoods will also need to play an active part:

◆ **Neighbourhoods could:**
  - secure community involvement
  - form local partnerships
  - establish a focal point for action
  - designate a flagship project
  - set clear objectives

One of the strongest messages to emerge from local projects studied is that securing the continuing commitment of local people and partner organisations is crucial to ensuring the sustainability of healthy neighbourhood projects. Those involved with starting up the project, both professionals and residents, will need to ensure that their plans, including HImPs, express local concerns and priorities and afford opportunities for widening the base of those involved. This will require some professionals to act in a way that takes them outside their own organisational "community", to become more a part of the neighbourhood they work in. There is a challenge for local people too. As projects develop and progress is made, a sense of ownership and empowerment will grow. The challenge will be to ensure that the project is tolerant and inclusive in its outlook, rather than becoming insular, exclusive or inflexible in its vision of the neighbourhood. Skilled facilitation, for instance by the development and support workers described above, will help to guard against this risk.

Neighbourhoods taking local action will need to establish effective partnerships and organisational structures to facilitate partnership working. Healthy schools and healthy workplaces as corporate bodies will already have many of the necessary administrative structures in place, and will be in a position to purchase services to support their initiatives in the usual way. Healthy neighbourhoods will need to find a way of operating that affords the necessary degree of organisation in terms of business functions and financial accountability. Care will need to be taken not to remove day to day responsibilities from local people who wish to be involved. And ways must be found that do not overlook the skills and experience residents could bring to the process. It will also be important to ensure that, as the project acquires a greater degree of organisation over time, it does not lose its ability to be responsive to local views. The scale and source of financial support, and the ways in which neighbourhoods are required to account for this to funders, will be influential in determining this process.

Neighbourhood projects will need to establish a focal point which provides a visible identity and a point of contact for other local organisations, residents and national level players. This need not necessarily be a centre open to the public, although some kind of administrative centre and an address will clearly be needed. Another key element in establishing a meaningful identity for neighbourhood projects will be the pursuit of at least one flagship project which directly addresses a pressing local issue, and which will attract the interest and support of local residents. This could take the form of action to improve local amenities, like the pond project in Beckton and the community shop in Matson. Of course, there may already be a local flagship project in the area as a result of another policy initiative - a Healthy Living Centre for example. The challenge will be for healthy neighbourhoods to ensure that such initiatives are consistent with local values and priorities, so that they join together to form a seamless strategy for health improvement.

It will be important for health and local authorities, together with other neighbourhood partner organisations, to recognise their responsibility to monitor the development of healthy neighbourhoods across the country. This will need to be considered in terms of how many neighbourhoods are becoming involved in local action, and their demographic structure, as well as the types of activity they are undertaking, the progress they are making, and the support needs they have – whether these are being expressed or not. This function should be strongly allied to the process of drawing up and monitoring Health Improvement Plans.

Neighbourhoods too, as a collective entity rather than as individual partner agencies, will need to be able to take stock of their progress at regular intervals. Being able to point to achievements will be important in maintaining motivation and commitment. And where progress has not been achieved, it is important that all of the neighbourhood level players reflect on why this has occurred, and what can be done to make things work better. To do this, neighbourhoods will need to set clear local objectives. In this way, all the partner organisations will be able to be quite clear about their involvement and responsibilities, as well as communicating their goals to individual residents, to Government and to national organisations. The objectives chosen will need to combine a mixture of short, medium and longer term criteria in order to balance the neighbourhood's vision for the future against the need for visible progress. Healthy neighbourhood projects have the potential to achieve significant health gains. It is important that information about their progress and impact is captured. So, what can local people do to support the development of healthy neighbourhoods?

◆ **People could:**
   - take responsibility for maintaining the positive aspects of their neighbourhood
   - get involved in local action
   - contribute their skills, knowledge and time

In their capacity as individual residents, people will be able to support healthy neighbourhood projects in a number of ways. Firstly, they can take responsibility for maintaining the positive aspects of their neighbourhoods, for instance by ensuring they do not pollute their neighbourhood with either noise or litter, or by informing neighbourhood management services swiftly of cases of vandalism or disrepair. More positively, there will be a range of ways that people can get involved in local action on healthy neighbourhoods: by attending groups, classes or meetings; by using facilities such as a community shop or a trading scheme; or by giving their views as part of a consultation exercise. Other people will wish to contribute more directly to the project, for example by offering practical help with administration, IT, or management or by using their local business contacts to provide support, sponsorship and materials. A healthy neighbourhood is one that recognises and values the contribution individual residents can make. Projects such as local enterprise trading schemes (LETS) could be instrumental in this process: one innovative model currently being piloted enables older people having difficulty maintaining their garden to obtain the services of a local resident, who in turn benefits from being allowed to use part of the garden to grow their own produce. Projects like this reinforce the idea that everyone in a neighbourhood has something to contribute. The success of the healthy neighbourhoods initiative will depend on the ability of local projects to harness this capacity and provide opportunities for local people to grow and develop their personal and practical skills as part of a process of health improvement.

Summary

Healthy neighbourhood projects are already being developed by residents and local agencies in many parts of the country, demonstrating the strengths of the neighbourhood setting as a focus for improving health and reducing health inequalities. Such activities are attracting growing interest from a wide range of organisations and sectors who recognise the value of engaging with local people to address the health issues concerning them. As the new public health strategy continues to develop, Government has the opportunity to recognise and support neighbourhood action, helping to build a comprehensive, effective and practical approach to improving the public health.

---

[48] *Our Healthier Nation*, op. cit., pp.18-19

APPENDIX ONE: Healthy neighbourhoods and health status:

The Report of the Independent Inquiry into Health Inequalities

Summary of recommendations

The Acheson report makes nearly forty detailed recommendations covering 12 different areas of policy[49]. This summary has been produced with the intention of highlighting those recommendations which have particular relevance to the healthy neighbourhood setting.

General Recommendations

1.   We recommend that as part of **health impact assessment**, all policies likely to have a direct or indirect effect on health should be evaluated in terms of their impact on health inequalities, and should be formulated in such a way that by favouring the less well off they will, wherever possible, reduce such inequalities.

1.1   We recommend establishing mechanisms to **monitor inequalities in health** and to evaluate the effectiveness of measures taken to reduce them.

1.2   We recommend a **review of data needs** to improve the capacity to monitor inequalities in health and their determinants at a national and local level.

2.   We recommend a high priority is given to policies aimed at improving health and reducing inequalities in **women of childbearing age**, expectant mothers and young children.

Poverty, income, tax and benefits

3.   We recommend policies which will further reduce **income inequalities**, and improve the living standards of households in receipt of social security benefits.

Housing and environment

10. We recommend policies which improve the **availability of social housing** for the less well off within a framework of environmental improvement, planning and design which takes into account **social networks**, and **access to goods and services**.

   [specific recommendations include...]

12.1 We recommend policies to improve insulation and heating systems in new and existing buildings in order to reduce further the prevalence of **fuel poverty**.

12.2 We recommend amending housing and licensing conditions and housing regulations on space and amenity to reduce **accidents in the home**, including measures to promote the installation of smoke detectors in existing homes.

13. We recommend the development of policies to reduce the **fear of crime** and violence, and to create a safe environment for people to live in.

Mobility, transport and pollution

14. We recommend the further development of a high quality **public transport** system which is integrated with other forms of transport and is affordable to the user.

16. We recommend further steps to reduce the usage of motor cars to cut the mortality and morbidity associated with **motor vehicle emissions**.

17. We recommend further measures to **reduce traffic speed**, by environmental design and modification of roads, lower speed limits in built up areas, and stricter enforcement of speed limits.

Nutrition

20. We recommend policies which will increase the availability and accessibility of foodstuffs to supply an adequate and affordable diet.

20.1 We recommend the further development of policies which will ensure adequate **retail provision of food** to those who are disadvantaged.

Mothers, children and families

21. We recommend policies which reduce poverty in families with children by promoting the material support of parents; by removing barriers to work for parents who wish to combine work with parenting; and by enabling those who wish to devote full-time to parenting to do so. Specifically:

21.1 We recommend an integrated policy for the provision of affordable, high quality **day care and pre-school education with extra resources for disadvantaged communities**.

22. We recommend policies which improve the **health and nutrition** of women of childbearing age and their children with priority given to the elimination of **food poverty** and the prevention and reduction of obesity.

22.3 We recommend the further development of programmes to help women give up **smoking** before or during pregnancy, and which are focused on the less well off.

23. We recommend policies that promote the social and emotional **support for parents and children**. Specifically:

23.1   We recommend the further development of the role and capacity of **health visitors** to provide social and emotional support to expectant parents, and parents with young children.

Young people and adults of working age

24.   We recommend measures to prevent **suicide** among young people, especially among young men and seriously mentally ill people.

26.1   We recommend policies which promote moderate intensity exercise including: further provision of **cycling and walking routes** to school, and other environmental modifications aimed at the safe separation of pedestrians and cyclists from motor vehicles; and **safer opportunities for leisure**.

Older people

28.   We recommend the quality of **homes** in which older people live be improved.

29.   We recommend policies which will promote the maintenance of **mobility**, **independence**, and **social contacts**.

Ethnicity

31.   We recommend that the needs of minority ethnic groups are specifically considered in the development and implementation of policies aimed at reducing socio-economic inequalities.

Gender

35.   We recommend policies which reduce **psychological ill-health** in young women in disadvantaged circumstances, particularly those caring for young children.

36.   We recommend policies which reduce disability and ameliorate its consequences in **older women**, especially those living alone.

The National Health Service

37.   We recommend that providing equitable access to effective care in relation to need should be a governing principle of all policies in the NHS. Priority should be given to the achievement of **equity** in the planning, implementation and delivery of services at every level of the NHS.

        [*specific recommendations include ...*]

37.3   We recommend developing the National Service Frameworks to address inequalities in access to effective **primary care**.

38.2   We recommend reviewing the size and effectiveness of the Hospital and Community Health Service (HCHS) formula and deprivation payments in influencing the health care outcomes of the most disadvantaged populations, and to consider alternative methods of **focusing resources** for health promotion and public health care to reduce inequalities.

39.1   We recommend there should be a duty of partnership between the NHS Executive and regional government to ensure that **effective local partnerships** are established between health, local authorities and other agencies and that joint programmes to address health inequalities are in place and monitored.

---

[49] D. Acheson, *Report of the Independent Inquiry into Inequalities in Health, op.cit.*

APPENDIX TWO: Housing quality

A series of criteria for identifying housing of a satisfactory quality has been provided by The Cost Effectiveness in Housing Investment Programme, who specify that housing should be assessed according to:

- space standards, occupancy levels and a reasonable level of privacy
- sound insulation, lighting, ventilation and heating arrangements
- facilities for food storage, preparation and consumption
- facilities for personal hygiene
- facilities for refuge storage and disposal
- the absence of worrying or damaging features such as dampness, noise, internal or external pollution and infestation
- the minimisation of the risk of accidents both inside the home and in the local area
- arrangements for the disabled or those with special needs (as appropriate)
- a sense of security both inside the home and in the local area
- access to home and contents insurance arrangements at acceptable cost
- the nature of the relationship with the owner (if rented housing)
- management standards and especially the speedy and satisfactory carrying out of repairs and maintenance
- a positive sense of empowerment, or at least participation in the organisation and management of the local environment, especially where major changes are occurring locally
- external recreational and other open space, both private and public for all age groups
- an acceptable visual appearance of both the accommodation and the local area
- the absence of any stigmatising or "ghettoising" factor
- the absence of neighbour problems and anti-social behaviour in the local area

- the proximity of low order retail and service facilities, transport facilities and necessary medical and educational services
- the nature, supportive or otherwise, of the local social community and networks
- an acceptable "cost-in-use" both in terms of occupancy costs and in the use of all the facilities listed[50]

[50] Source: P. Ambrose, *I Mustn't Laugh Too Much, op. cit.*, pp9-10.

BIBLIOGRAPHY

D. Acheson, *Report of the Independent Inquiry into Inequalities in Health*, The Stationery Office, 1998.

L.Arblaster, M.Hawtin, "Health, housing and social policy", Socialist Health Association, 1993, cited in *Report of the Independent Inquiry into Inequalities in Health,* ibid

P. Ambrose, Barlow J. et.al., *The Real Cost of Poor Homes*, Royal Institute of Chartered Surveyors, 1996

P. Ambrose, *I Mustn't Laugh Too Much: Housing and Health on the Limehouse Fields and Ocean Estates in Stepney*, Centre for Urban and Regional Research, University of Sussex, 1996

D. Black, "Glasgow: working together to make a healthier city", *World Health*, 49:1, Jan-Feb 1996.

Beckton Community Health Project, *Annual Review 1997/98*

Best, R. "The Housing Dimension", in Benzeval, Judge and Whitehead, eds., *Tackling Inequalities in Health*, London, The King's Fund, 1995.

M. Barrow and R. Bachan, 1997, *The Real Cost of Poor Homes: Footing the Bill*, Royal Institute of Chartered Surveyors

R. Best, "The Housing Dimension", in Benzeval, Judge and Whitehead, eds. "Tackling inequalities in health: an agenda for action", The King's Fund, 1995

Camden Healthy Cities Project, *Quality of Life Conference for Older People and their Carers*, Report of a conference held on 21.9.96, London, 1996

Community Development Foundation, *Involving Children in Neighbourhood Regeneration*, a briefing paper for Chief Executive Departments of Local Authorities, 1998.

Department for Education and Employment, *Meeting the Childcare Challenge*, The Stationery Office, London, May, 1998.

Department of Health Circular dated 30th December 1997

Department of Health Circular dated 3rd July 1998

Department of Health, *Our Healthier Nation: a contract for health,* London, The Stationery Office, 1998.

Department of the Environment, Transport and the Regions, *Sustainable Local Communities for the 21st Century: Why and how to prepare an effective local agenda 21 strategy,* February 1998

Department of Transport, Environment and the Regions, *New Deal for Communities, Phase 1 Proposals: Guidance for Applicants*, 15th September 1998

Department of Transport, Environment and the Regions, *Sustainability Counts*, November 1998

Department of Health, 1998, *Healthy Living Centres: Report of a seminar held on 2nd April 1998*

Elizabeth Harris and Jenny Wills, "Developing healthy local communities at local government level: lessons from the past decade", *Australian and New Zealand Journal of Public Health*, 1997, 21:4

Greg Goldstein and Ilona Kickbusch, "A healthy city is a better city", *World Health*, 49:1, Jan-Feb 1996 and The World Health Organisation, *Sustainable Development and Healthy Environments, Programme for the Promotion of Environmental Health: Settings for Health*, http://www.who.int/peh/hlthcit/setting.htm (20.11.98)

Health Education Authority with the Local Government Association, *Health on the Agenda? A guide to health strategy development for local authorities*, London, HEA, 1997

Health Education Authority, *Community Action for Mental Health*, London, 1998

Heartsmart report, *Gardening for Health in the Bradford District*, produced by Bradford District Health Promotion Service

Home Office, *Supporting Families: A consultation document*, The Stationery Office, London, 1998.

A. Scriven and S. Young, "Health promotion, Environmental Health and Agenda 21", *Journal of the Royal Society of Health*, April 1998, 118; 2, 85-90

A. Stallibrass, *Being Me and Also Us: Lessons from the Peckham experiment*, Scottish Academic Press, Edinburgh, 1989

Shell Better Britain Campaign Project Profile 33, *Gardening for Health*, May 1998

Social Exclusion Unit, *Bringing Britain Together: a national strategy for neighbourhood renewal*, HMSO, Cm 4045, September 1998

A. D. Tsouros, "A nine year investment", *World Health*, 49:1, Jan-Feb 1996
A.Whelan, R.Mohr, S.Short, "Waving or drowning? Evaluation of the National Secretariat, Healthy Cities Australia", Sydney: Australian Community Health Association, 1992 cited in WHO Healthy Cities Programme, *Sustainable Development and Healthy Environments, Programme for the Promotion of Environmental Health*, http://www.who.int/peh/hlthcit/, (20.11.98)

World Health Organisation Regional Office for Europe *Health 21 – The Health for All Policy for the European Region – 21 Targets for the 21st Century*, Copenhagen, 1998

World Health Regional Office for Europe, *Twenty steps for developing a Healthy Cities project*, Copenhagen, 1992.